CLOSE-UP

Chris Jones & Alex Ball

THE NATURAL HISTORY MUSEUM

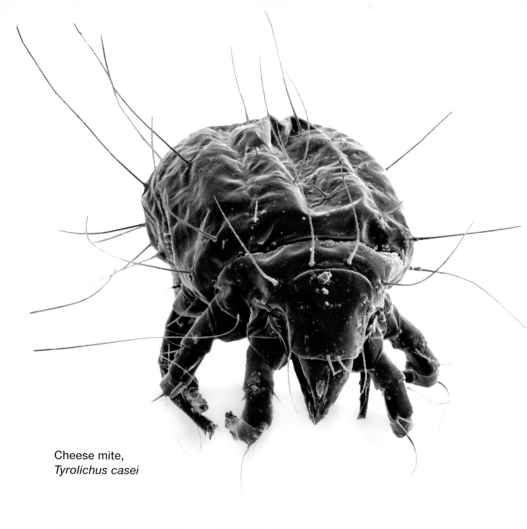

Cheese mite,
Tyrolichus casei

The images in this book were taken using scanning electron microscopes (SEMs), and show the stunning beauty and complexity of the surface structures of objects, at once both familiar and strange. In many cases the magnifications of the photographs are rather modest (a few hundred times life-size), but the detail they reveal is unobtainable with any other microscopy technique.

There are a number of factors which combine to produce these remarkable images. The SEM scans a tightly focussed beam of electrons, in a vacuum, over the sample. The area scanned can be smaller than the wavelength of visible light, so very high levels of detail can be revealed at high magnifications. As the beam interacts with the specimen, electrons within the object's surface are emitted, collected and displayed on a screen to form an image which can be photographed or digitally recorded. However, because the electron beam has a much shorter wavelength than visible light, there is no colour information and the SEM can only produce a black and white image. Some of the images seen in this book have been coloured using a computer, and this technique is often used to highlight features of interest or simply for aesthetic reasons.

SEMs can also produce low-powered images with a depth of field much greater than a light microscope, which means that most of the

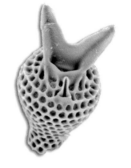

sample stays in focus. Images can also be produced of very reflective, or transparent objects since the SEM does not 'see' through the specimen and the electron beam used to image the sample is not reflected from shiny surfaces.

All SEMs require a vacuum to operate. This is because the electron beam would otherwise be absorbed or scattered by gases in the sample chamber. Traditionally, this means that the sample needs to be preserved, dried and coated with an ultra-fine layer of metal or carbon. Recent technological advances allow a reduction in the vacuum levels of some types of SEM, so the sample can be examined without any preparation. This is a huge advantage if the scientist needs to examine material which is unique, delicate or has to be kept in its original state.

The scanning electron microscope has always played an important role in research, where close-up views of intricate structures reveal differences between similar species. Technological advances in SEMs have improved our ability to examine a wider range of specimens than ever before, allowing more precise and meaningful identification and classification, whilst enhancing our understanding of the natural world.

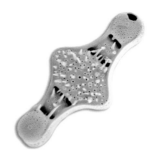

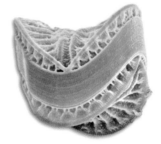

Diatoms are tiny, single-celled, aquatic organisms, which photosynthesize. Their cell walls are made of silica, producing a rigid, box-like structure. Left from top: *Gladius, Amphipentas, Glyphodiscus* and right from top: *Biddulphia, Campylodiscus, Triceratium.*

Seven-spot ladybird, *Coccinella 7-punctata*

The seven-spot ladybird is the most common species of ladybird in the UK. Newly-emerged adults have yellow wing-cases, which darken to red as the exoskeleton hardens. These tough wing-cases resist most insect attacks, and ladybirds are able to secrete a foul-tasting yellow liquid from their joints if threatened by larger predators. Birds and animals soon learn to associate the bright red colour with a bad taste and will even avoid any other similarly coloured insects.

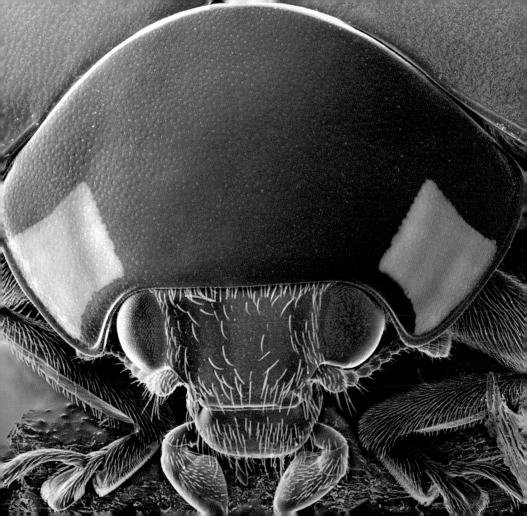

Honey bee mite, *Varroa destructor*

This mite, which originates from Asia, is a parasite of honey bees, including the European honey bee *Apis mellifera*. The female mite with its oval, flattened body, just 1.1–1.2 mm long, lays her eggs in the cells of developing bees so that the young mites can feed on their blood. Feeding weakens the bees and leaves them open to infection, and the hive becomes less viable. Honey bees are pollinators of agricultural crops, so a lack of pollination at the appropriate time prevents the plants from developing seed, affecting the next season's crop.

9

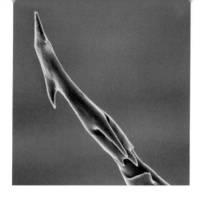

Radula tooth of the cone snail, *Conus californicus* and radula teeth of blue australwinkle, *Austrolittorina unifasciata*

In most snails there is a tongue-like structure covered in teeth called radulae. In some snails the radulae are highly-specialised for a carnivorous diet, such as in the *Conus* species (above). This marine snail inhabits the shores of the American west coast. It has a single harpoon-like tooth held at the tip of the proboscis which carries a powerful poison. It stabs its prey – including other snails, worms and small fish - and death from the venom follows within seconds. In contrast to this is the marine australwinkle (right), found on temperate Australian seashores. It uses its file-like ribbon of teeth to rasp the microscopic blue-green algae covering the rocks. The entire radula may be up to ten times the length of the 15 mm snail, and lies tightly coiled within the body.

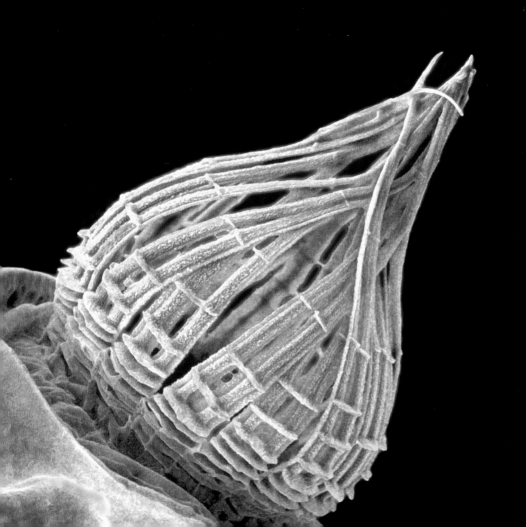

Tip of moss spore capsule, *Rhizogonium novae-hollandiae*

This moss is found in Australia and New Zealand, where it grows on shaded trunks of trees and tree ferns or on rotting wood lying on the forest floor. The fringe of tooth-like projections surrounding the opening of the spore capsule is called the peristome. The outer 'teeth' move inwards and outwards in response to changes in moisture and thus regulate the release of the spores.

Black bean aphid, *Aphis fabae*

Aphids have sucking mouthparts and feed on the sap of plants, sometimes causing enormous damage. Their colonies can include both winged and wingless adults, and many species have life cycles with alternating asexual and sexual phases. The development of asexually reproducing individuals may be so rapid that new-born nymphs already contain the developing embryos of their own progeny-to-be. With the entire life cycle taking as little as one week, the potential for explosive population growth is great. Many aphids have developed a symbiotic relationship with ants. The ants provide the aphids with protection in return for the aphids' excreta, which is called 'honeydew' because it consists mainly of sugary plant sap.

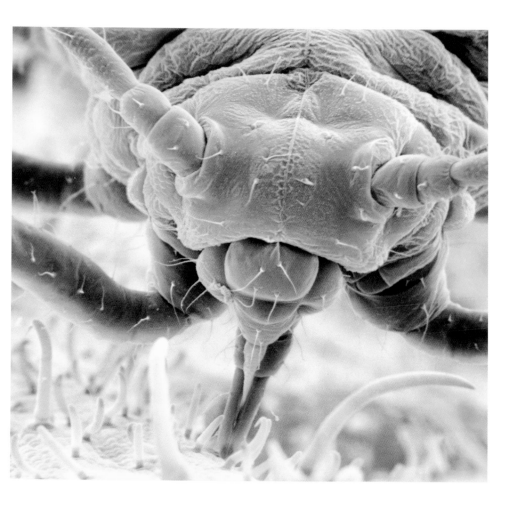

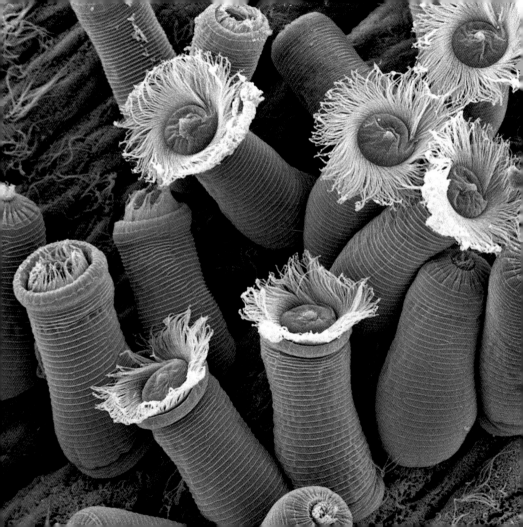

Ciliate, *Scyphidia physarum*

Ciliates are single-celled protozoans found worldwide. This species lives on aquatic hosts, usually without causing them any harm. Some species of *Scyphidia*, however, can be extremely pathogenic, damaging the skin of fish, sometimes killing them. The individuals shown are attached to the extended body of the freshwater snail *Physa fontinalis*. *Scyphidia* is a filter-feeder, and the beating action of the rows of hair-like cilia sweep particulate matter such as bacteria into the mouth.

Larder beetle, *Dermestes lardarius*

This insect pest can subsist on almost anything, and has been known to eat cereals, grains, dairy products and meat as well as hide, bone, horns, hooves, hair, wool and feathers. The larvae, which are the most destructive phase, excavate pupation chambers prior to metamorphosing into adults, which can live for up to a year. In museums, dermestid beetles are used to clean animal and bird carcasses to reveal the skeletons.

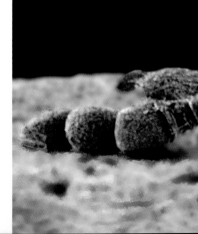

Tapeworm, *Amirthalingamia macracantha*

Tapeworms are parasites that can infest the gut of many species of vertebrates. The means by which they are attached varies, but a crown of hooks is common in tapeworms of birds and mammals. Tapeworms absorb nourishment through their skins and have no alimentary canal or mouth. *Amirthalingamia macracantha* is found as a larva in the liver of the freshwater fish *Tilapia nilotica* or Nile tilapia, and as an adult in the great cormorant, *Phalacrocorax carbo*. It has been recorded in Mali, Sudan, South Africa and Kenya.

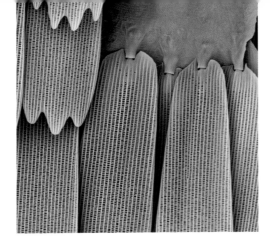

Wing and head of small tortoiseshell butterfly, *Aglais urticae*

The head of a butterfly is dominated by its huge compound eyes. Its wings and body are covered by thousands of tiny scales (above). These improve its aerodynamics, and help with temperature regulation. They also produce the butterfly's colour pattern, built up, scale by scale, like the pixels of a digital image. Most scales are simply coloured by containing pigment. The iridescent colours seen in some butterflies, including many tropical species, are produced by the three-dimensional structures of special scales that only reflect particular wavelengths of light. The long, coiled proboscis (right) enables the butterfly to feed by sucking nectar from flowers.

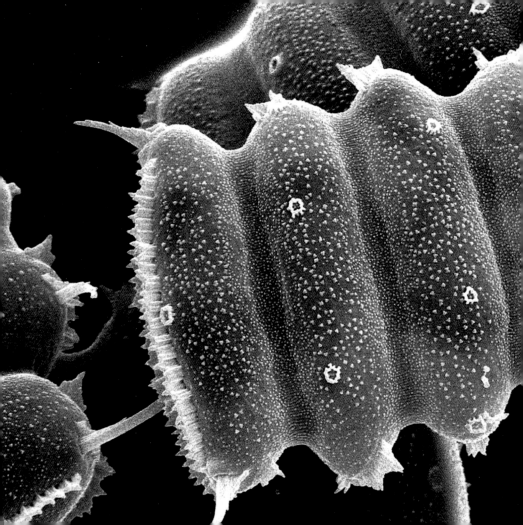

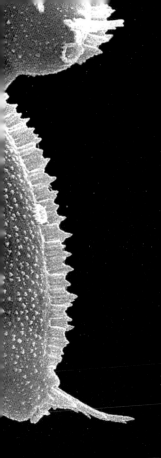

Algae, *Desmodesmus armatus*

Green algae are microscopic, single-celled or multi-celled organisms, invisible to the naked eye, yet found in aquatic and terrestrial environments worldwide. They are photosynthetic and are at the very base of the food chain, providing a food source for zooplankton and some fish. The alga shown here is multi-celled made up of four cells linked together, with spines protruding from its surface. These spines are made up of long, hollow structures, resembling a clutch of drinking straws, and improve flotation as well as acting as a defence against grazing by zooplankton. This species can also be single-celled, and can be used as a model for helping scientists understand the origin of multi-cellularity, a basic evolutionary process.

25

Black garden ant, *Lasius niger* and South American jumping ant, *Gigantiops destructor*

The foot of the black garden ant (above), has two large claws for grasping and a suction disc enabling it to walk on the underside of glossy leaves. The huge eyes of the 8 mm long South American jumping ant (right) enable it to run down prey, such as termites, and to avoid danger. The ants can detect an approaching person at several metres, and they will rapidly run and jump away. The majority of ants use chemical markers to orientate themselves, whereas this species uses visual markers and can memorize relatively complex routes.

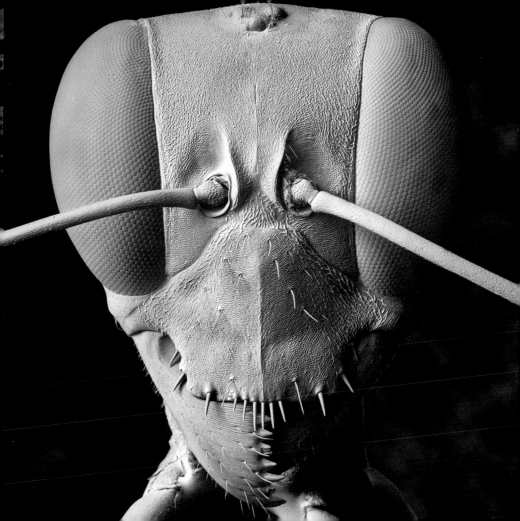

Scales of mosquito, *Trichoprosopon digitatum* and malaria mosquito, *Anopheles gambiae*

The densely-packed scales on the mosquito's back (left) are also seen on spiders and butterflies. Found in the tropical region of South and Central America, this species breeds in plant cavities and is unique in that it broods its eggs. It is not medically important and, unlike the malarial mosquito, it does not bite humans. The malaria mosquito (below) is found in sub-Saharan Africa and is the world's worst malaria vector. It lives in close association with humans and breeds in groundwater, which makes it extremely difficult to control by the elimination of breeding places. The entire genome of this mosquito has been sequenced, which should make it possible to develop new ways of preventing malaria transmission.

Coccolithophores

These oceanic phytoplankton produce an external skeleton of calcareous plates or coccoliths, probably primarily for protection. After the death of the organism these coccoliths sink to the sea floor and accumulate to form the main component of deep ocean sediments. Many show bizarre morphological adaptations such as the extraordinary trumpet-like structures of *Discosphaera tubifera* (top left) and the intricate interlocking plates of *Acanthoica quattrospina* (right). One of the most ubiquitous organisms on Earth is *Emiliania huxleyi* (top middle) which frequently forms blooms in the north Atlantic and North Sea, giving the water a milky hue. Many coccolithophores such as *Calcidiscus leptoporus* (top right) produce two different types of coccoliths during their life cycle. The image represents a transition in this cycle, showing the fusion of two sex cells from which a daughter cell emerges to form a different coccolith layer.

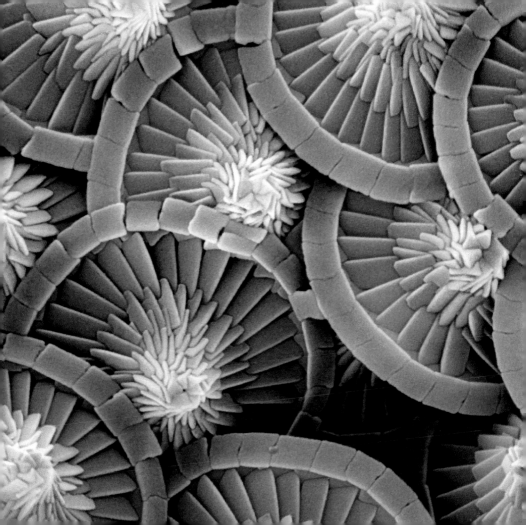

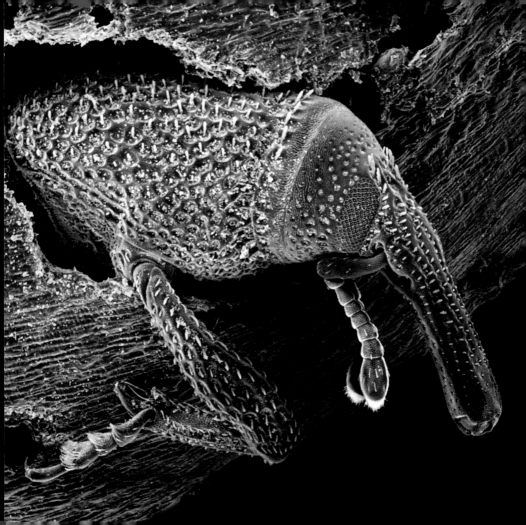

Grain weevil, *Sitophilus granarius*

Adult grain weevils are 3-4 mm long and are serious pests of stored food. Each egg is laid in a hole chewed out of a single grain. When the egg hatches the larva hollows out the grain as it feeds and develops, finally emerging as an adult to mate and begin the cycle again. The complete life cycle takes around 30-40 days and adult weevils can live for 6-7 months.

Schistosome, *Schistosoma nasale*

The adults of this parasitic flatworm grow up to 11 mm in length and feed on the blood in the nasal veins of cattle, sheep, goats and water buffalo in India, Sri Lanka, Burma and Bangladesh. The adult male holds the female in a special muscular groove as shown here. Eggs laid in the nasal veins of the host cause inflammation and tissue proliferation leading to large cauliflower-like growths. This causes nasal schistosomiasis, or 'snoring disease', and breathing difficulties. *Schistosoma nasale* is the only known mammalian schistosome that preferentially selects the nasal veins of its hosts.

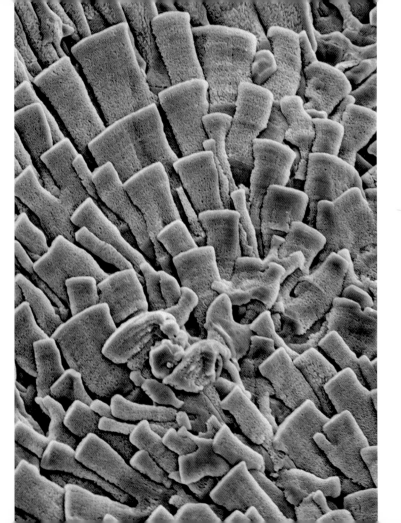

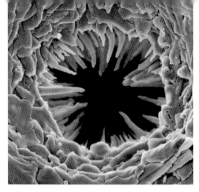 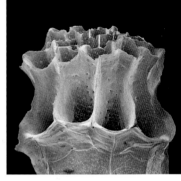

Bryozoan, *Cinctipora elegans*

Bryozoans are animals which live as colonies, often secreting skeletons that form crusty masses. Some are free-living, others are attached to a hard surface such as a mollusc shell or a rock. Their skeletons are made up of tiny crystals which can grow as plates overlapping like tiles on a roof (left). Individuals within the colony are connected through a series of pores in the skeleton (top left). Bryozoan individuals have tentacles which emerge from openings (top right), and can be withdrawn when they detect danger. The signal to withdraw their tentacles can be passed from individual to individual via the pores. Complete colonies of this New Zealand species can grow up to 20 cm in height.

Common wasp worker, *Vespula vulgaris*

Wasps are social insects that live in colonies ruled by a single queen. Unlike bees, however, wasps are carnivorous, and their strong mandibles are used for pulling apart and chewing wood, which they mix with saliva to make the papery walls of the colony's nest. Inside the nest, the queen lays her eggs in cells and workers care for the developing larvae. Workers also forage for food and defend the nest. At the end of the year, the queen abandons the nest, overwinters in a sheltered spot and forms a new colony in the spring. The nest is never used again and those workers which remain will not survive the winter.

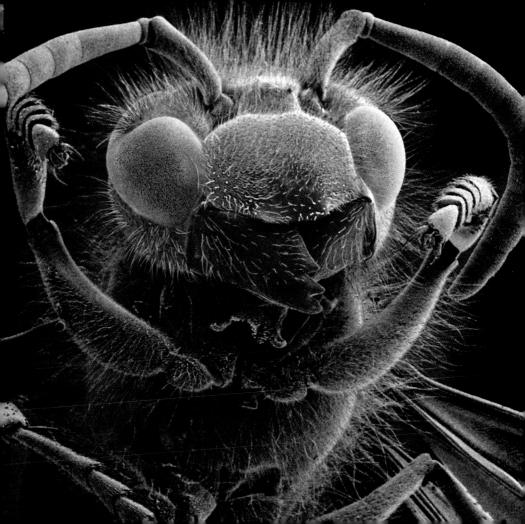

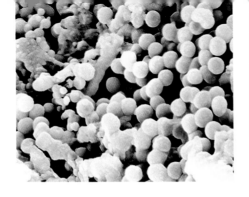
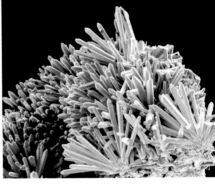

Galena, opal and mattheddleite

Galena (left), a lead sulphide, is the most important lead ore. Found throughout the world, it is a significant source of silver. Its silvery-grey cubic crystals are identical in structure to those of table salt (sodium chloride), but denser. Precious opal (top left) is a silica gel composed of tightly-packed microscopic balls. The spaces between the balls create a range of colours due to refraction of light like a prism. If the spacing is equal, one colour is seen, e.g. the red of a fire opal; if the spacing is variable the light will be refracted into a number of wavelengths giving rise to different colours or opalescence. Mattheddleite, a lead silicate, is named after the 19th century Scottish geologist, Matthew Heddle. The crystals (top right) develop radially or in the form of a rosette, and are usually colourless or pale blue.

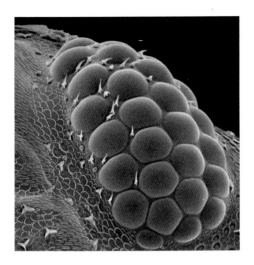

Pill woodlouse, *Armadillium vulgare*

Woodlice are terrestrial crustaceans that can live only in damp environments because they breathe by means of gills, which must remain covered in a thin film of water. Paradoxically, woodlice that fall into water quickly drown. Pill woodlice have heavy, calcified shells and are commonly found in close association with human habitation since lime mortar and stonework provide a ready supply of chalk. Woodlice can live for 3–4 years and produce young throughout most of the summer.

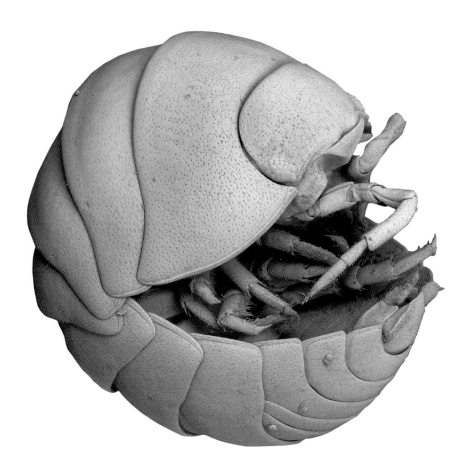

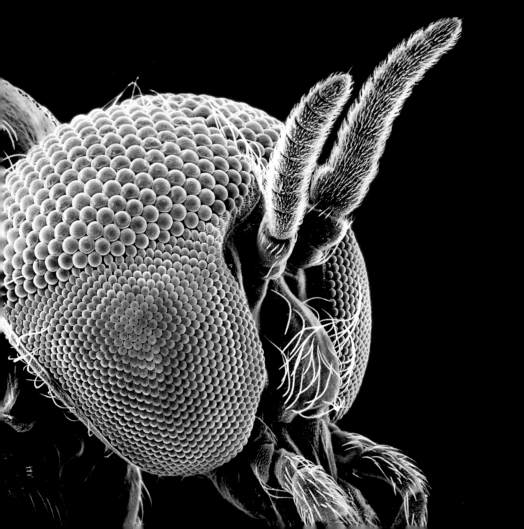

Black fly, *Simulium* spp.

Most of the head of the male black fly is covered by a pair of compound eyes. This is because sexual recognition relies largely on vision. The males only feed on nectar and do not have biting mouthparts. The females, however, have biting mouthparts and feed on nectar and blood. Female black flies emerging from their breeding grounds in flowing water are a nuisance in temperate regions, where their irritating bites cause misery to campers and fishermen. In the tropics, however, they have a more serious impact as the carrier of a parasitic round worm (nematode) that causes human onchocerciasis (river blindness).

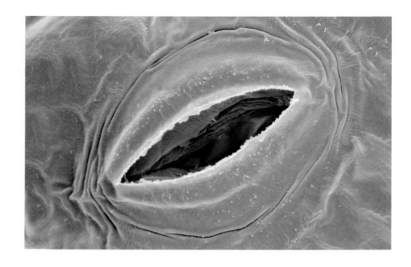

Underside of *Pelargonium* leaf

Small glands attached to the *Pelargonium* leaf hairs contain an essential oil, which is released if the leaf is brushed. The hairs on the leaves also deter insects by impeding their movement over the leaf surface. Stomata or breathing pores (above) allow the exchange of oxygen for carbon dioxide to take place within the leaf's tissues, but also contribute to the loss of water vapour. Guard cells at the edge of the stomata can expand to close the pore when water is scarce.

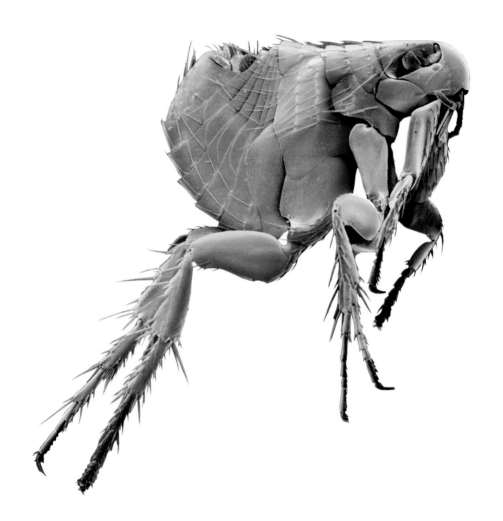

Oriental rat flea or plague flea, *Xenopsylla cheopis*

Fleas are 1-8 mm long, wingless, blood-sucking parasites. They have hard, flattened bodies and powerful back legs that enable them to jump from host to host. The Oriental rat flea prefers to feed on black rats but it will also bite humans and this is how the bubonic plague (or Black Death) that ravaged Europe and Asia from the 14th to 17th centuries, was spread. Black rats carried fleas infected with the plague bacterium *Yersinia pesti* into towns and cities and the fleas then infected people.

Box mite, *Phthiracarus* spp.

Members of this genus are found all over the world, apart from the extremes of the Arctic and Antarctic. Their feeding breaks down plant matter, helping decomposition. When threatened they completely withdraw their legs and mouthparts into the main part of the exoskeleton and the shield covering the mouthparts forms the 'lid' of the 'box'. Despite this behaviour, box mites still end up as prey for reptiles and amphibians.

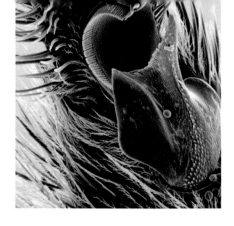

European honey bee worker, *Apis mellifera* and red-tailed bumble bee, *Bombus lapidarius*

Honey bees are social insects that form colonies comprising a single queen, several drones and some 60-70,000 workers. Only the queen and the drones are sexually mature. The queen secretes a pheromone throughout her active life which suppresses the sexual development of the workers. The workers build the beehive combs, forming hexagonal cells from wax produced by glands on their abdomens. They use the cells for storing nectar and pollen, and housing the developing larvae. The workers tend to the larvae, clean and aerate the hive, forage for food and defend the nest. The comb on the foreleg of this red-tailed bumble bee (above) is used to remove pollen and other matter on the sensory organs of the antennae.

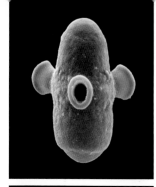

Pollen

Pollen grains show enormous variation in structure. The distinctive pollen of the whorlflower, *Morina longifolia* (top left), from the Himalayas, has a funnel-shaped protrusion of the wall around each of the pores. Popularly known as 'windowsill geraniums', the pollen grains of the *Pelargonium* species (right) are characterised by a distinctively wrinkled surface. The grain of the yellow monkey flower, *Mimulus luteus*, from Chile has two interlocking parts, like a tennis ball (left). Those of the yellow water lily, *Nuphar lutea*, are covered with long conical spines that hold them together in masses, like burs (bottom left). This may help cross-fertilization by sticking to the flies and other insects that pollinate its flowers.

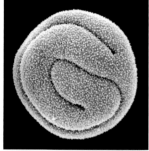

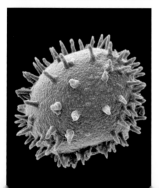

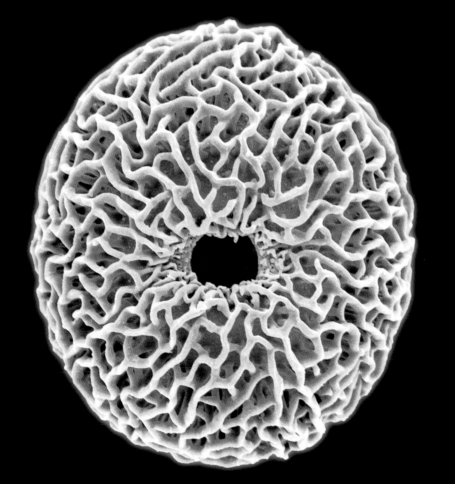

Zebra jumping spider, *Salticus scenicus*

Like other spiders, jumping spiders have eight eyes, but the front four eyes are enlarged and arranged in a line to give excellent stereo vision over a range of 20-30 cm. Although the position of the eyes is fixed, the front-facing eyes have a complex muscle system that enables the spider to move the retina relative to the lens so that it can look in slightly different directions. The other eyes, positioned on the sides of the carapace provide peripheral vision.

Egg of the louse, *Solenopotes burmeisteri* on red deer hair, and human head louse, *Pediculus humanus capitus*

Lice are parasitic insects which live amongst hairs and feed on blood; they are unable to survive longer than 24 hours when separated from their host. The eggs or 'nits' are glued onto the hairs near to the base (above) and are very difficult to remove. Adult lice live for little over a month and the female may lay 50-150 eggs in her lifetime which hatch in 5-9 days. Lice move slowly and are unable to jump, so they spread from one host to another when the hosts are in contact with each other, or if the louse falls into bedding which is then occupied by another member of the host species. Head lice (right) live amongst the hairs on the head, and those associated with the body, or pubic hair belong to different species. Head lice have strong claws on their feet which are shaped to grip the hairs on the head.

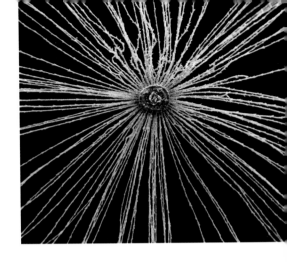

Dandelion, *Taraxacum officinale*

Dandelions are native to Europe and related to sunflowers. The name *dandelion* means 'lion's teeth' and comes from the French *dent de lion*, referring to the plant's serrated leaves. The yellow flowerheads are composed of a large number of florets arranged on a receptacle. Each floret produces a bottle-shaped, single-seeded fruit topped by a tuft of fine hairs (left). When the fruit is mature the neck of the 'bottle' elongates and the seed is blown away dangling beneath its parachute (above).

Skin of lesser spotted dogfish, *Scyliorhinus canicula* (above) and smoothhound shark, *Mustelus mustelus* (right)

Shark skin is covered with tiny 'teeth' called dermal denticles; each species has denticles of a different shape as can be seen here. The denticles protrude from the skin and are aligned so that they channel water across the shark's body in the most efficient way. If you run your hand across shark skin in one direction it is smooth, in the other it is abrasive. The dermal denticles may help to improve the efficiency of the shark by reducing drag and allowing the shark to 'slide' through the water more smoothly.

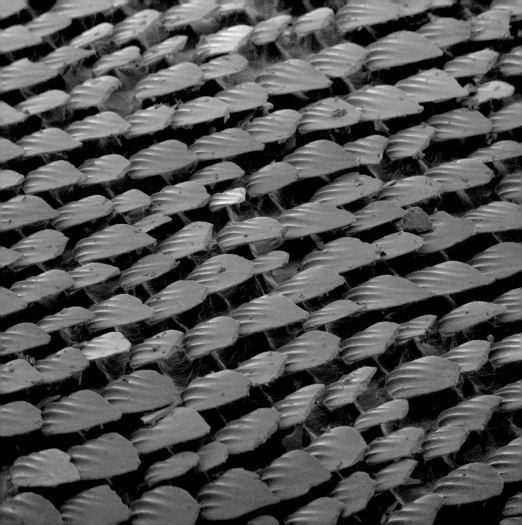

Magnifications of images in this book

p.2, 300x; p.4 (top) 1350x, (middle) 550x, (bottom) 940x; p.5 (top) 940x, (middle) 1000x, (bottom) 650x; p.7, 60x; p.8, 220x; p.10, 530x; p.11, 1250x; p.12, 200x; p.13, 100x; p.15, 240x; p.16, 1300x; p.19, 100x; p.20, 250x; p.22, 400x; p.23, 70x; p.24, 9000x; p.26, 460x; p.27, 60x; p.28, 282x; p.29, 70x; p.30 (left) 1500x, (middle) 3500x, (right) 1500x; p, 31, 38,000x; p.32, 120x; p.35, 100x; p.36, 8000x; p.37 (left) 2700x, (right) 24x; p.39, 50x; p.40, 120x; p.41 (left) 15,000x, (right) 38x; p.42, 140x; p.43, 25x; p.44, 2200x; p.46, 2200; p.47, 260x; p.48, 80x; p.51, 240x; p.52, 14x; p.53, 130x; p.54 (top) 1800x, (middle) 1100x, (bottom) 1100x; p.55, 1700x; p.56, 65x; p.58, 30x; p.59, 120x; p.60, 45x; p.61, 40x; p.62, 44x; p.63, 60x; end papers 2800x.

Picture credits

p.30 Markus Geisen
All other images are copyright of the Natural History Museum, London, and available from the Picture Library at http://piclib.nhm.ac.uk/piclib/www/

Acknowledgements

With special thanks to the following for their help: Anne Baker, Neil Bell, Barry Bolton, Rod Bray, Ralph Harbach, Paul Hillyard, Theresa Howard, Jon Martin, Andrzej Massalski, David Reid, Elliot Shubert, Tony Shelley, Vaughan Southgate, Peter Stafford, John Taylor, Paul Taylor, Dick Vane-Wright, Alan Warren, David Williams and Jeremy Young.

First published by the Natural History Museum, Cromwell Road, London SW7 5BD
© 2004, The Natural History Museum, London
ISBN 0-565-09172-7

Edited by: Celia Coyne
Designed by: Dina Koulama
Digital colouration: Harry Taylor
Reproduction and printing by: Craft Print, Singapore
End papers: Anther of daisy, *Bellis perennis*

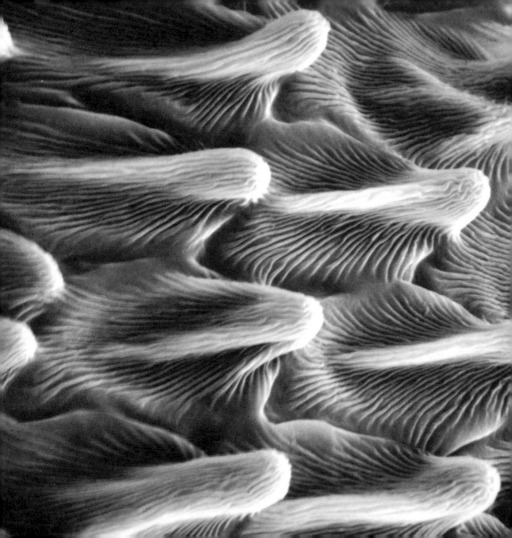